The Learning Works

Cover Design & Illustration:
Kelly Kennedy

Text Design and Editorial Production:
Kimberley A. Clark

Creative Teaching Press, Inc.
Huntington Beach, CA 92649

Library of Congress Catalog Number: 95-076635
ISBN: 0-88160-232-9

> **This book is dedicated to John and Sarah.**

Contents

Contents
(continued)

Music and Songs

Contents
(continued)

Oodles of Fun While You Wait
© The Learning Works, Inc.

Introduction

Oodles of Fun While You Wait is designed to make time spent waiting pass more quickly and promote parent-child interaction at the same time. The clever activities challenge the mind while providing hours of fun. The topics have been divided into several categories:

- **On the Road** activities will improve both geography and observational skills.

- **Entertainment** tests your recollection of movie and television characters, titles, and plot lines.

- **Sports** offers the opportunity for sports enthusiasts to recall sports figures past and present, team names, sports, positions, and equipment used.

- **Music and Songs** leads you down memory lane as you remember song titles, lyrics, and artists; and allows you to show off your songwriting and singing talents!

- **Word Brain Teasers** challenge you to brainstorm lists of words in a variety of categories while increasing your vocabulary.

- **Storybook Characters and Such** deals with children's literature of all kinds from nursery rhymes and fairy tales to Dr. Seuss and Newbery classics.

License Plate Scavenger Hunt

Take a look at the license plates on the cars you see as you travel. Find one that has *three* letters on it. Keeping the letters in the same order, how many words can you make? You may add letters at the beginning, at the end, or between the original letters, as long as their order remains the same.

Example: **325HAL**
KENTUCKY   halt, whale, lethal, health

Warm-ups:

1.	ALC	6.	CRA
2.	BAR	7.	AKE
3.	TRO	8.	STR
4.	SOL	9.	ORN
5.	TRE	10.	PAL

Challenge:

Try a real license plate and ask your fellow passengers to help you create and write down as many words as possible.

Triple Threat

Jot down the numbers you see on three consecutive road signs. Add them together.

Example:

Route 55
Brenton — 43 mi.
12 MPH
$55 + 43 + 12 = 110$

Challenge:

Keep trying until you get a sum that fits each of the following categories. Use each category one time and play until all the categories have been found.

1. a number greater than 50
2. a triple digit sum
3. an odd sum
4. an even sum
5. a sum with a zero in it

Oodles of Fun While You Wait
© The Learning Works, Inc.

Find a Job

While you are riding in the car, look out the car windows and try to find a person whose job requires him or her to . . .

1. drive or ride in a special vehicle.
2. work outdoors.
3. work with animals.
4. wear a uniform.
5. work high above the ground.
6. stand or sit in one spot for a long time.
7. wear a helmet.
8. work alone.
9. help other people.
10. collect money.
11. drive other people around.
12. work with something hot.
13. do the same thing over and over.
14. write something down.
15. move objects from one place to another.

U.S. Landmarks

In what U.S. state or district is each of the following
famous attractions or landmarks located?

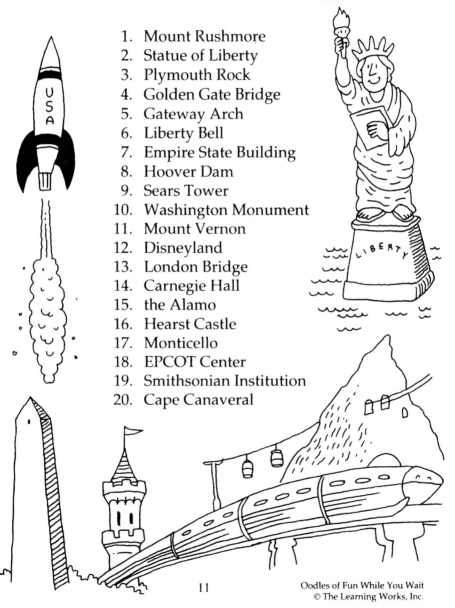

1. Mount Rushmore
2. Statue of Liberty
3. Plymouth Rock
4. Golden Gate Bridge
5. Gateway Arch
6. Liberty Bell
7. Empire State Building
8. Hoover Dam
9. Sears Tower
10. Washington Monument
11. Mount Vernon
12. Disneyland
13. London Bridge
14. Carnegie Hall
15. the Alamo
16. Hearst Castle
17. Monticello
18. EPCOT Center
19. Smithsonian Institution
20. Cape Canaveral

Naturally Wonderful

Can you name the state in which each
of these natural wonders is found?

1. Niagara Falls
2. Grand Canyon
3. Great Salt Lake
4. Death Valley
5. Mt. McKinley
6. Pike's Peak
7. Carlsbad Caverns
8. Old Faithful
9. Everglades Swamp
10. Mammoth Cave
11. Lake Okeechobee
12. Okefenokee Swamp
13. Mauna Loa
14. Craters of the Moon
15. Yosemite Valley
16. Mojave Desert
17. Cape Cod
18. Finger Lakes
19. Crater Lake
20. Mt. Ranier

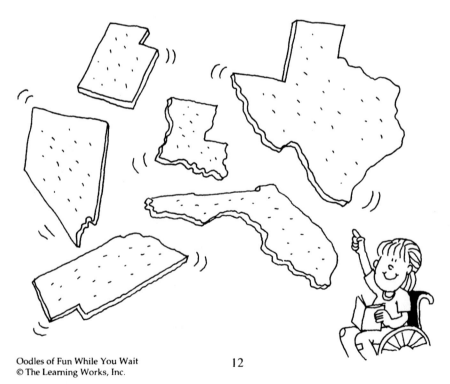

State It in Words

There are, of course, cities in every state. But did you know that there are also words in every state? All you need for this game is a U.S. map or a list of the 50 states.

Here's your challenge: List as many words as you can using the letters in each state name. All the words you brainstorm must be correctly spelled and the letters should appear in the same order as they did in the state name.

Examples:

Oregon → or, ore, ego, go, on
Alaska → a, alas, la, as, ask

Warms-ups:

Try to create a list of your own using
- Washington
- New Hampshire
- Mississippi

Challenge:

Make this game even more challenging by searching for words in the names of countries, rivers, lakes, mountain ranges, or other geographical locations. Which name produces the longest list of words? Challenge your friends or family members to top your list!

13

Oodles of Fun While You Wait
© The Learning Works, Inc.

On the Town

As you scan a road map of any state, you may be surprised by some of the unusual place names that you'll find. Some are "colorful" names such as Blue, Arizona; Orange, Texas; or Violet, North Carolina. Other names are comical. Have you ever heard of Eek, Alaska; Tumtum, Washington; or Slapneck, Michigan? Use a road map of any state for the following activity.

Warm-ups:

Find the name of a city or town that fits each of the following categories:

- a "colorful" name (e.g., Red Lake, AZ)
- an animal name (e.g., Bumble Bee, AZ)
- a famous person's name (e.g., Geronimo, AZ)
- a girl's name (e.g., Katherine, AZ)
- the name of an object (e.g., Moccasin, AZ)

Challenge:

Examine your road map to see how long a list of towns you can come up with for each of the following categories. An example has been given for each.

three-letter names	Why, AZ
occupations	Barber, NY
presidential names	Coolidge, NM
names with numbers	Eighty Four, PA
weather names	Sunny Vale, NC
boy's names	Jerome, AZ
nonsense names	Twisp, WA
foreign names	Peru, NC

WELCOME
TO

WHY

ARIZONA

Vehicle Patrol

How keen are your powers of observation? Imagine that you're a member of the vehicle patrol and you're looking for stolen vehicles with the following identifying features:

1. a dented fender
2. two bumper stickers
3. a college emblem in the window
4. a suction-cup animal in the rear window
5. fuzzy dice hanging on the rear-view mirror
6. a flat tire
7. a red light on top
8. three people in the back seat
9. the top down
10. the hood up
11. a driver who is talking on the phone
12. an advertisement painted on the door
13. a dog inside
14. a car dealer's license plate
15. a baby or toddler in the back seat

Oodles of Fun While You Wait
© The Learning Works, Inc.

Busy Bodies

Consider this: At the same time you're riding along in the car, millions of other people are doing something completely different. Look out the car windows and try to spot someone who is . . .

1. mowing the lawn.
2. jogging.
3. swinging.
4. riding a bike.
5. walking.
6. carrying a briefcase.
7. digging.
8. playing ball.
9. eating.
10. painting.
11. sitting on a bench.
12. climbing a ladder.
13. gardening.
14. delivering mail.
15. swimming.
16. working on a car.
17. walking a dog.
18. directing traffic.
19. washing a car.
20. selling something.

Signs of the Times

It's pretty amazing how much information we get from all the signs posted along the road. On your next trip, keep an eye out for the types of signs listed below. Also see if you can spot others not listed here.

1. One Way
2. Yard Sale
3. House for Sale
4. For Rent
5. No U-Turn
6. Private Property
7. Posted: No Trespassing
8. Yield
9. No Hunting
10. Beware of Dog
11. No Parking
12. Keep off the Grass
13. School Crossing
14. Railroad Crossing
15. No Turns
16. Road Closed
17. Speed Limit
18. Truck Crossing
19. Cattle Crossing
20. political campaign poster
21. Population
22. Welcome

Oodles of Fun While You Wait
© The Learning Works, Inc.

Bumper Sticker Bonanza

You can learn a lot about people from the bumper stickers on their cars. For example, in election years, many bumper stickers indicate a car owner's favorite candidate. Spend a car ride looking for interesting bumper stickers.

Try to spot one with . . .

1. a political campaign ad.
2. a radio station logo.
3. the name of a school or college.
4. a person's picture.
5. a sports team name.
6. the name of a state.
7. the name of a city.
8. the name of an organization.
9. an anti-drug message.
10. a number.
11. the name of a business.
12. more than six words.
13. a picture of an animal.
14. the name of a church.
15. an American flag.
16. a humorous message.
17. a famous quotation.
18. a rhyme.

Get to Work

How many of the following workers can you spot?

1. police officer
2. crossing guard
3. telephone line worker
4. fire fighter
5. truck driver
6. gas station attendant
7. toll collector
8. bus driver
9. street vendor
10. construction worker
11. window washer
12. carpenter
13. roofer
14. sanitation worker
15. mechanic
16. ambulance driver
17. fast food worker
18. parking attendant
19. gardener
20. painter

In a Word

Try to identify a road sign or billboard containing . . .

1. a three-letter word.
2. a color word.
3. north, south, east, or west.
4. the name of a state.
5. the words *up* or *down*.
6. a word in all capital letters.
7. flashing lights.
8. an abbreviation.
9. an arrow.
10. only one word.
11. a misspelled word.
12. the words *left* or *right*.
13. a phone number.
14. a person's name.
15. moving parts.

Riddles for the Road

How familiar are you with United States geography? Answer each of the following riddles with the name of one or more U.S. states.

1. I am the smallest state.
2. I am the largest state.
3. I have more people than any other state.
4. I am a state that is divided into two parts.
5. I am a state made up of a group of islands.
6. I am a peninsula.
7. I touch only one other state.
8. I touch no other states.
9. I touch the Atlantic Ocean.
10. I touch the Gulf of Mexico.
11. I touch both the Atlantic Ocean and the Gulf of Mexico.
12. I touch the Pacific Ocean.
13. I touch Mexico.
14. I touch both the Pacific Ocean and Mexico.
15. I touch Canada.

State of Being

Name the U.S. state or states whose names have . . .

1. two syllables.
2. a direction word (north, south, east, west).
3. two words.
4. three syllables.
5. double consonants.
6. double vowels.
7. the same first and last letter.
8. a vowel at the beginning.
9. a vowel at the end.
10. eight letters.

What's in a Name?

There certainly are some strange names for the cars people drive. How many models of cars can you think of that have a . . .

1. mammal's name?
2. bird's name?
3. four-letter name?
4. five-letter name?
5. name that is a compound word?
6. name beginning and ending with the same letter?
7. name containing a double consonant?
8. name containing a double vowel?
9. one-syllable name?
10. two-syllable name?
11. three-syllable name?
12. foreign name?
13. name with numbers or initials in it?
14. name beginning with "c"?
15. name ending with "e"?

Oodles of Fun While You Wait
© The Learning Works, Inc.

Wheeling Along

How many of the following vehicles can you spot?

1. four-door car
2. delivery truck
3. tow truck
4. school bus
5. ambulance
6. motor home
7. police car
8. taxi
9. motorcycle
10. moped
11. dump truck
12. tractor-trailer
13. moving van
14. mail truck
15. tour bus
16. car towing a boat
17. fire truck
18. tanker truck
19. bicycle
20. horse trailer

Entertainment

Animal Actors

Many of the most famous on-screen personalities aren't people at all—they're animals. Can you supply the animal last name of each of these celebrities?

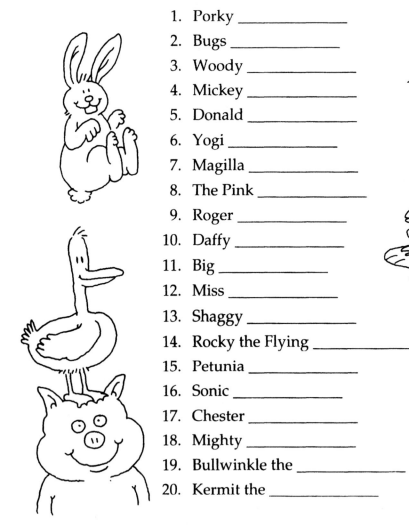

1. Porky _____
2. Bugs _____
3. Woody _____
4. Mickey _____
5. Donald _____
6. Yogi _____
7. Magilla _____
8. The Pink _____
9. Roger _____
10. Daffy _____
11. Big _____
12. Miss _____
13. Shaggy _____
14. Rocky the Flying _____
15. Petunia _____
16. Sonic _____
17. Chester _____
18. Mighty _____
19. Bullwinkle the _____
20. Kermit the _____

Name That Kid

Can you name the following television kids? Give the character's name from the show.

1. Andy Taylor's son on "The Andy Griffith Show"
2. Ben Cartwright's three sons on "Bonanza"
3. The three kids on "Roseanne"
4. Danny Tanner's three daughters on "Full House"
5. The five Cosby kids
6. The three Winslow kids on "Family Matters"
7. The annoying neighbor on "Full House"
8. The pesky neighbor on "Family Matters"
9. The seven kids on "The Waltons"
10. The six kids on "The Brady Bunch"
11. The Cunningham kids on "Happy Days"
12. The three sons on "Home Improvement"
13. The youngest son on "Wonder Years"
14. The two kids on "Who's the Boss?"
15. The three Seaver kids on "Growing Pains"

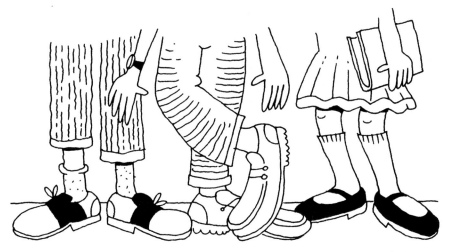

Oodles of Fun While You Wait
© The Learning Works, Inc.

Home Sweet Home

Every television series has a setting. For instance, "Superman" put the fictional city of Metropolis on the map. "The Beverly Hillbillies" brought us to—where else?—Beverly Hills, California. Can you name the television series that takes place in each of these real or imaginary locations?

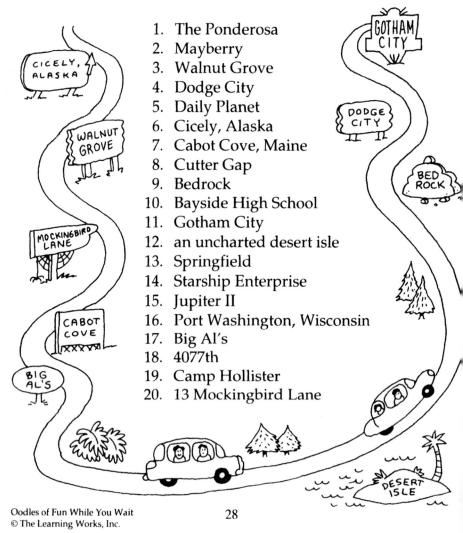

1. The Ponderosa
2. Mayberry
3. Walnut Grove
4. Dodge City
5. Daily Planet
6. Cicely, Alaska
7. Cabot Cove, Maine
8. Cutter Gap
9. Bedrock
10. Bayside High School
11. Gotham City
12. an uncharted desert isle
13. Springfield
14. Starship Enterprise
15. Jupiter II
16. Port Washington, Wisconsin
17. Big Al's
18. 4077th
19. Camp Hollister
20. 13 Mockingbird Lane

Mystery Titles

Name as many television shows as you can that have . . .

1. a number in the title.
2. a woman's name in the title.
3. a man's name in the title.
4. a one-word title.
5. the name of a city in the title.
6. the name of an animal in the title.
7. mother, father, mom, dad, mommy, or daddy in the title.
8. an occupation in the title.
9. initials or an abbreviation in the title.
10. the word "and" in the title.
11. an apostrophe in the title.
12. a color word in the title.
13. an "-ing" word in the title.
14. a plural word in the title.
15. two-word titles in which both words begin with the same letter.

29

Sidekicks

Half of each famous—or infamous—duo is missing. Can you supply the name of the missing partner?

1. _____ & Ernie
2. Lewis & _____
3. _____ & Jerry
4. Abbott & _____
5. _____ & Mutley
6. Batman & _____
7. Gumby & _____
8. Regis & _____
9. _____ & Wile E. Coyote
10. _____ & Roebuck

11. Mork & _____
12. _____ & Mr. Hyde
13. _____ & Hardy
14. Bonnie & _____
15. Hansel & _____
16. Mutt & _____
17. Pebbles & _____
18. Siskel & _____
19. Chip & _____
20. Cagney & _____

Something in Common

What does each trio of characters have in common?

1. Lone Ranger, Batman, Zorro
2. Ben Matlock, Perry Mason, Claire Huxtable
3. Dumbo, Peter Pan, Mighty Mouse
4. Potsie, Ralph, Fonzie
5. Huey, Dewey, Louey
6. Kermit the Frog, Oscar the Grouch, Incredible Hulk
7. Ginger, Mary Ann, The Professor
8. Scooby Doo, Pluto, Odie
9. Hoss, Little Joe, Adam
10. Curly, Larry, Moe
11. Alvin, Simon, Theodore
12. Lucy, Pigpen, Linus
13. Uncle Fester, Wednesday, Pugsley
14. Chester, Doc, Miss Kitty
15. Donatello, Raphael, Michelangelo

Fun and Names

On what TV show would you find each of these animal or human characters?

1. Fonzie
2. Beaver
3. Comet
4. Potsie
5. Cockroach
6. Avery
7. Six
8. Hawkeye
9. Screech
10. Goober
11. Sully
12. Doogie
13. Barkley
14. Radar
15. John Boy
16. Nub
17. Lurch
18. Bull
19. Meathead
20. Morticia

Movie Madness

What animal name will complete
each of the following movie titles?

1. "The Mighty _____"
2. "Who Framed Roger_____?"
3. "That Darn _____"
4. "_____ Dundee"
5. "Dances With _____"
6. "101 _____"
7. "The Great _____ Detective"
8. "_____ Man"
9. "The Shaggy _____"
10. "They Shoot _____, Don't They?"
11. "One Flew Over the _____'s Nest"
12. "Clarence, the Cross-Eyed _____"
13. "The _____ King"
14. "The Pink _____"
15. "To Kill a _____"

It's Just a Job

Television imitates life in many ways. For instance, most of the adult characters on your favorite TV series have some kind of job. Can you name the profession of each of these TV characters?

1. Alice on "The Brady Bunch"
2. Mike Brady on "The Brady Bunch"
3. Cliff Huxtable on "The Cosby Show"
4. Barney Fife on "The Andy Griffith Show"
5. Howard Cunningham on "Happy Days"
6. Wood Newton on "Evening Shade"
7. Carl Winslow on "Family Matters"
8. Nils Olsen on "Little House on the Prairie"
9. Tony Micelli on "Who's the Boss?"
10. The title character on "Murphy Brown"
11. Danny Tanner on "Full House"
12. Tim Taylor on "Home Improvement"
13. The title character on "Big Brother Jake"
14. The title character on "Perry Mason"
15. Ginger on "Gilligan's Island"

Name That Number

Each of the following book, movie, and song titles can be completed by placing a number in the blank. How many do you know?

1. _____ Penny Box

2. The _____ Balloons

3. _____ Dalmatians

4. Ramona Quimby, Age _____

5. The _____ Dresses

6. _____ Trombones

7. _____ Little Indians

8. _____ Brides for _____
   Brothers

9. Snow White and the _____ Dwarfs

10. Around the World in _____ Days

11. Miracle on _____th Street

12. _____ Men and a Baby

13. _____: A Space Odyssey

14. _____ Blind Mice

15. _____ Days of Christmas

Oodles of Fun While You Wait
© The Learning Works, Inc.

It's Not Easy Being Green

What color is each of the following characters?

1. Big Bird
2. Barney
3. Oscar the Grouch
4. Cookie Monster
5. Kermit
6. Tweety
7. Snoopy
8. Woodstock
9. Incredible Hulk
10. Odie

11. Frosty
12. Papa Smurf
13. Grover
14. Miss Piggy
15. Casper
16. Fozzie
17. Daffy
18. Grinch
19. Garfield
20. Winnie the Pooh

Friend or Foe?

What well-known character hangs around with each of the following characters? Are they friends or foes?

1. Bluto
2. Baby Bop
3. Boo Boo
4. Robin
5. Ernie
6. Miss Piggy
7. Odie
8. Elmer Fudd
9. Minnie Mouse
10. Petunia Pig

11. Barney Rubble
12. Rocky the Flying Squirrel
13. Eeyore
14. Tom
15. Mr. Wilson
16. Sylvester
17. Wile E. Coyote
18. Snoopy
19. Christopher Robin
20. Yosemite Sam

37

Movie Trios

In which movie can you find each
of the following trios of characters?

1. Jasmine, Abu, Jafar
2. Gepetto, Jiminy Cricket, Stromboli
3. Thumper, Flower, Faline
4. Mrs. Jumbo, Timothy Q. Mouse, bullies
5. Merlin, Wart, Archimedes
6. Cheshire Cat, March Hare, Queen of Hearts
7. Sebastian, Ariel, Flounder
8. Fairy Godmother, Prince, stepsisters
9. Simba, Pumbaa, Mafatu
10. Perdita, Pongo, Cruella de Vil
11. Belle, Mrs. Potts, Gaston the Hunter
12. Maleficent, Merryweather, Briar Rose
13. Wendy, Tinker Bell, Captain Hook
14. Lady Marian, Little John, Sir Hiss
15. Sneezy, Bashful, Sleepy
16. Jock, Trusty, Jim Dear
17. Baloo, Mowgli, Bagheera
18. Thomas O'Malley, Duchess, Scat Cat

Three's a Crowd

On what TV show can you find each of these trios of characters?

1. Thurston Howell, III; the Professor; the Skipper
2. Mr. Wilson, Joey, Ruff
3. Granny, Jethro, Jed
4. Nellie Olsen, Almanzo Wilder, Miss Beadle
5. Fred Mertz, Ethel Mertz, Ricky Ricardo
6. Herman, Lily, Eddie
7. Morticia, Uncle Fester, Lurch
8. Ralph Kramden, Ed Norton, Trixie Norton
9. Aunt Bee, Gomer, Floyd the barber
10. Ike Godsey, Mamie Baldwin, Yancy Tucker
11. Radar, Colonel Potter, Hawkeye
12. Tootie, Mrs. Garrett, Natalie
13. Della Street, Lieutenant Tragg, Paul Drake
14. Ralph Malph, Marian Cunningham, Jenny Piccolo
15. Archie, Edith, Meathead

Oodles of Fun While You Wait
© The Learning Works, Inc.

Reel News

Extra! Extra! Read all about it! Hollywood movie plots become front page news! Each of the following headlines reflects the plot of a well-known movie. How many can you identify?

1. Yellow Brick Road Paves the Way to a Magical Land
2. Backwoods Family Strikes It Rich; Moves to Beverly Hills
3. Desperate Dad Poses as Nanny to Spend Time with Kids
4. Young Son Left Behind While Family Goes on Vacation
5. Trio of Homesick Pets Finds Way Back to Loved Ones
6. Boy Befriends Wolf as He Searches for Lost Gold Mine
7. Nutty Inventor Creates Flying Automobile
8. Scientist Dad Accidentally Shrinks Offspring
9. Boy Enters Dogsled Race to Raise Money for College
10. Three Friends Go on Cattle Drive to Cure Depression
11. Young Boy Meets Lovable Creature from Outer Space
12. Ancient Spell Turns Boy into Sheepdog
13. Adopted St. Bernard Puppy Goes from Cute and Cuddly to a Catastrophic 185 Pounds
14. Four Children Are Transported into Mythical Land of the Evil Ice Queen
15. Theme Park Security System Goes Haywire; Dinosaurs Go on Rampage

And the Winner Is...

Every sport has competitions, tournaments, and awards. With what sport is each of the following associated?

1. Super Bowl
2. World Series
3. Stanley Cup
4. Kentucky Derby
5. World Cup
6. PBA National Championship
7. Indianapolis 500
8. Heisman Trophy
9. Tour de France
10. Firestone Tournament of Champions
11. U.S. Open
12. Daytona 500
13. America's Cup
14. Masters Tournament
15. Cy Young Award
16. Wimbledon
17. British Open
18. Golden Gloves Tournament
19. Davis Cup
20. Preakness Stakes

Name That Sport

How much do you *really* know about sports? Enough to be a network sports commentator? Here's a chance to test your technical knowledge. Name the sport or sports associated with each of these terms:

1. free throw
2. rebound
3. bunt
4. field goal
5. takedown
6. sack
7. point after
8. punt
9. slap shot
10. face-off

11. body check
12. butterfly
13. side out
14. on deck
15. bogey
16. uppercut
17. escape
18. lob
19. par
20. spare

Oodles of Fun While You Wait
© The Learning Works, Inc.

U.S. Olympic Gold

In which sport did each of these U.S. Olympic athletes bring home the gold medal?

1. Kristi Yamaguchi
2. Dan Jansen
3. Carl Lewis
4. Bonnie Blair
5. Shannon Miller
6. Janet Evans
7. Greg Louganis
8. Peggy Fleming
9. Jesse Owens
10. Mary Lou Retton
11. Dorothy Hamill
12. Oscar De La Hoya
13. Jennifer Capriati
14. Mark Spitz
15. Michael Jordan
16. Bart Conner
17. Matt Biondi
18. Gail Devers
19. Florence Griffith-Joyner
20. Bruce Jenner

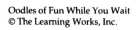

Birds of a Feather

Name the city or state that is home to each of the following "high-flying" sports teams:

1. Cardinals
2. Penguins
3. Falcons
4. Hawks
5. Orioles
6. Eagles
7. Seahawks
8. Suns
9. Blue Jays
10. Flyers

11. Blackhawks
12. Jets
13. Rockets
14. Hornets
15. Stars
16. Red Wings
17. Astros
18. Angels
19. Lightning
20. Flames

45

Team Names

How many professional sports teams can you think of whose names fit the following categories?

1. four-letter words
2. color word in name
3. mammals
4. number in name
5. two-word place name (example: *New York* Jets)
6. compound word in name
7. "-ing" in name
8. two-word names
9. double consonant in name
10. two-syllable names
11. "er" in name
12. only one vowel in name
13. three-syllable name
14. name that begins with a vowel
15. name that doesn't end in "s"

Famous Figures from the World of Sports

Name the sport with which each
of these sports legends is associated.

1. Yogi Berra
2. Johnny Weissmuller
3. Wilma Rudolph
4. Terry Bradshaw
5. Johnny Bench
6. Evelyn Ashford
7. Jack Nicklaus
8. Olga Korbut
9. Dorothy Hamill
10. Arnold Palmer
11. Joe Frazier
12. Bonnie Blair
13. Tracy Austin
14. Ty Cobb
15. Mario Andretti
16. Martina Navratilova
17. Sonja Henie
18. Reggie Jackson
19. Mildred "Babe" Didriksen
20. Gail Devers

47

Scrimmage Scramble

Unscramble the following to yield
20 terms related to football.

1. httig den
2. isugrhn
3. kbtreurcqaa
4. seffoids
5. nowcohtud
6. feereer
7. veerecri
8. delduh
9. baserorcdo
10. ytfase

11. tunpre
12. txare tipon
13. inkgips
14. irgrnodi
15. tohfur wnod
16. yenlapt
17. celats
18. longhid
19. lendice
20. melteh

In Position

Ever heard of a football pitcher? A baseball linebacker? Try to name the correct sport for each of the following players.

1. tight end
2. jockey
3. placekicker
4. center
5. shortstop
6. quarterback
7. wicketkeeper
8. coxswain
9. free safety
10. goalie
11. cornerback
12. guard
13. batsman
14. right wing
15. sweeper
16. right fielder
17. center halfback
18. running back
19. heavyweight
20. punter

385

49

Necessary Equipment

With which sport or sports is each
of the following equipment associated?

1. paddle
2. tee
3. quiver
4. wicket
5. cue
6. shuttlecock
7. wedge
8. pommel horse
9. pins
10. discus
11. rings
12. arrow
13. face mask
14. hurdle
15. puck
16. stick
17. baton
18. putter
19. flights
20. mat

World Class Athletes

These familiar athletes come from all over the world. Can you name each athlete's country?

1. Linford Christie
2. Alberto Tomba
3. Katarina Witt
4. Jean-Claude Killy
5. Franz Klammer
6. Boris Becker
7. Kristin Otto
8. Viktor Petrenko
9. Jayne Torvill
10. Steffi Graf
11. Nadia Comaneci
12. Wayne Gretzky
13. Pelé
14. John Newcombe
15. Sergei Bubka
16. Bjorn Borg
17. Olga Korbut
18. Sonja Henie
19. Margaret Smith Court
20. Bobby Orr

51

More Sports Terms

Name the sport or sports in which each of these terms in used.

1. kickoff
2. dribble
3. infield fly
4. icing
5. T-formation
6. jump ball
7. neutral zone
8. traveling
9. frame
10. lob

11. putt
12. foul line
13. placekick
14. fairway
15. runback
16. line of scrimmage
17. checking
18. squeeze play
19. end zone
20. touchback

Sports Mix-Up

Each word or group of words can be unscrambled to name a sport. How many can you uncover?

1. band hall
2. mob and tin
3. foal bolt
4. flog
5. in nest
6. my castings
7. Able's lab
8. blast Blake
9. own glib
10. Brad is ill.

11. glue
12. bed slob
13. welt rings
14. class ore
15. a cherry
16. caring shore
17. a taker
18. band hall
19. C. C. Rose
20. Pete's sad king

Oodles of Fun While You Wait
© The Learning Works, Inc.

Team Spirit

How many professional sports team names can you put in a single sentence? Try making a sentence using the team names given. Then make up some sentences using teams of your choice.

Example:

Cardinals have *Red Wings.*

1. Rangers, Red Sox
2. Lightning, Jets, Flames
3. Suns, Heat, Senators
4. Whalers, Oilers, Blackhawks
5. Bucks, Nets, Bullets
6. Senators, Penguins, Flyers
7. Timberwolves, Indians, Cowboys
8. Mavericks, Broncos, Twins
9. Magic, Giants, Clippers
10. Dolphins, Raiders, Pirates

Triple Play

One member of each of the following trios is out of place. Two of the people in each group are associated with the same sport, but the third does not belong. How many misfits can you find?

1. Bobby Orr   Bobby Hull   Bobby Unser
2. Rick Barry   Barry Sanders   Barry Foster
3. Jack Dempsey   Jack Johnson   Jack Kemp
4. Joe Namath   Joe Montana   Joe DiMaggio
5. Bruce Jenner   Bruce Smith   Emmitt Smith
6. Jim Brown   Jim Kelly   Jim Courier
7. Mike Ditka   Dick Butkus   Dick Button
8. Frank Reich   Frank Robinson   Frank Gifford
9. Brooks Robinson   Jackie Robinson   Sugar Ray Robinson
10. "Babe" Ruth   "Red" Grange   "Dizzy" Dean
11. Ty Cobb   Tai Babilonia   Cy Young
12. Willie Stargell   Willie Shoemaker   Willie Mays
13. Gale Sayers   Hale Irwin   Dale Earnhardt
14. Reggie Jackson   Reggie White   Lorenzo White
15. Joe Louis   Joe Frazier   Joe Greene

More Sports Legends

Name the sport in which each
of these legendary figures played.

1. Babe Ruth
2. Midori Ito
3. Bart Starr
4. Jerry West
5. Michael Jordan
6. Nancy Lopez
7. Jimmy Connors
8. Jackie Robinson
9. Joe DiMaggio
10. Billie Jean King
11. Sam Snead
12. Richard Petty
13. Evonne Goolagong
14. Julianne McNamara
15. Emmitt Smith
16. Monica Seles
17. Larry Bird
18. Bobby Orr
19. Steffi Graff
20. Wilt Chamberlain
21. Roberto Clemente
22. Muhammad Ali
23. Arthur Ashe
24. Sugar Ray Leonard
25. Mickey Mantle
26. Kristi Yamaguchi
27. A. J. Foyt
28. Arnold Palmer
29. Debi Thomas
30. Steve Young

Music and Songs

Famed Song Characters

Name the song character that fits each
of the following descriptions.

1. He stuck a feather in his hat.
2. She could bake a cherry pie.
3. Her shoes were number nine.
4. It was short and stout.
5. Her old, grey goose was dead.
6. He was the magic dragon.
7. He played nick-nack on my thumb.
8. He lives in Drury Lane.
9. They go up and down, up and down, up and down.
10. They were all in a row.
11. He washed his face in the fryin' pan.
12. She is a spunky gal.
13. Someone's in the kitchen with her.
14. He rowed the boat ashore.
15. He was a steel-drivin' man.
16. He hopped down the bunny trail.
17. He came marching home.
18. Was he sleeping, was he sleeping?
19. He was a fairy tale, they say.
20. He's comin' to town.

BUNNY TRAIL

Who Goes There?

What name completes the title of each song below?

1. When _____ Comes Marching Home
2. _____ Had a Little Lamb
3. _____ , the Red-Nosed Reindeer
4. My Darling _____
5. _____ Boy
6. Oh, _____
7. _____ Cottontail
8. _____ , Row the Boat Ashore
9. Skip to My _____
10. Old _____ Clark
11. Go Tell Aunt _____
12. _____ the Knife
13. My _____ Lies Over the Ocean
14. Old _____ Tucker
15. _____ Crack Corn

Where?

Do you know where . . .

1. the farmer lived?
2. grandfather's clock stood for 90 years?
3. you should put a penny when Christmas is coming?
4. the little puffer bellies stand in a row?
5. the five little ducks went to play?
6. the birds and beasts were?
7. Billy Boy had been?
8. the watermelons grow?
9. this old man played three?
10. you row, row, row your boat?
11. Yankee Doodle went?
12. I went to see my Sal?
13. the bear went?
14. the eensy, weensy spider climbed?
15. the little star twinkled?

Next, Please . . .

Sing each of these opening lines and add the line that follows.

1. There was a farmer had a dog . . .
2. Oh, I went down South for to see my Sal . . .
3. You are my sunshine, my only sunshine . . .
4. I've been workin' on the railroad . . .
5. I'm a little teapot, short and stout . . .
6. I went to the animal fair . . .
7. Down by the bay . . .
8. On top of spaghetti, all covered with cheese . . .
9. Down by the station, early in the morning . . .
10. All around the mulberry bush . . .
11. Doe, a deer, a female deer . . .
12. I wish I was in the land of cotton . . .
13. Oh, give me a home, where the buffalo roam . . .
14. Row, row, row your boat . . .
15. If I had a hammer . . .

Oodles of Fun While You Wait
© The Learning Works, Inc.

Animals in Song

Name the animal or animals that
each of these song lines is describing.

1. The old lady swallowed one, but I don't know why.
2. She ain't what she used to be.
3. He went a courtin'.
4. He's in the window, but I don't know how much he is.
5. He sat in the old gum tree.
6. He went over the mountain.
7. He was the farmer's dog.
8. If the looking glass gets broke, papa will buy you this.
9. His ears were cut short and his tail cut long.
10. She'll be driving them when she comes.
11. They sat on a curbstone shooting dice.
12. They ran after the farmer's wife.
13. They went out to play, over the hill and far away.
14. He climbed up the water spout.
15. He scooped up field mice and bopped 'em on the head.
16. He ruled the others with a quack, quack, quack.
17. He knows the way to carry the sleigh.
18. He chased the weasel around the mulberry bush.
19. They were baked in a pie.
20. He combed his hair by the light of the moon.

Name That Tune

How many songs can you name whose titles contain . . .

1. the first line of the song.
2. a question.
3. a number word.
4. a color word.
5. "big" or "little".
6. "old" or "new".
7. a person's first name.
8. only one word.
9. a contraction.
10. the name of a city or state.
11. rhyming words.
12. "up" or "down".
13. "in" or "out".
14. an animal name.
15. a nonsense word.

Be a Songwriter

See if you can come up with original lyrics for each of these simple, familiar tunes.

1. Happy Birthday
2. Jingle Bells
3. I'm a Little Teapot
4. Mary Had a Little Lamb
5. Frosty, the Snowman
6. Row, Row, Row Your Boat
7. Twinkle, Twinkle Little Star
8. Yankee Doodle
9. London Bridge
10. The Eensy, Weensy Spider

11. Bingo
12. The Farmer in the Dell
13. If You're Happy and You Know It
14. For He's a Jolly Good Fellow
15. Rockabye, Baby
16. Do, Re, Mi
17. Over the River
18. America the Beautiful
19. Rudolph, the Red-Nosed Reindeer
20. This Old Man

What in the World?

Can you name each of the following things
found in children's song?

1. The cow jumped over it.
2. It was over the river and through the woods.
3. Froggie carried them by his side when he went a courtin'.
4. Lucy Locket lost hers.
5. What the bear saw when he went over the mountain.
6. Old King Cole called for these.
7. The lamb's fleece was as white as this.
8. Some like it hot and some like it cold.
9. What Johnny promised to bring home from the fair.
10. The kookaburra sat in one.
11. The black sheep had three of them.
12. If you have no daughters, you can give them to your sons.
13. Dear Liza had a hole in hers.
14. Bobby Shaftoe wore them at his knee.
15. What Aunt Rhody was saving the old, grey goose to make.

Oodles of Fun While You Wait
© The Learning Works, Inc.

Movie Tunes

What movie made each of the following songs popular?

1. A Whole New World
2. A Spoonful of Sugar
3. Bibbidi-Bobbidi-Boo
4. Under the Sea
5. Chim Chim Cher-ee
6. Whistle While You Work
7. Zip-A-Dee-Doo-Dah
8. Give a Little Whistle
9. Heigh-Ho
10. Supercalifragilisticexpialidocious
11. Waltz of the Flowers
12. If I Only Had a Heart
13. My Favorite Things
14. Somewhere Out There
15. Hakuna Matata

Missing Links

Each of the following singers or vocal groups has part of its name missing. How many can you complete?

1. Steely _____
2. The Doobie _____
3. Tom Petty and the _____
4. Carly _____
5. Garth _____
6. The Beach _____
7. The Grateful _____
8. Whitney _____
9. Reba _____
10. _____ Clapton
11. _____ G
12. Stone Temple _____
13. Elton _____
14. _____ Manilow
15. Boyz II _____
16. Pearl _____
17. Elvis _____
18. Led _____
19. Fleetwood _____
20. The Rolling _____

67

Golden Oldies

Can you complete each of
the classic rock and roll song titles below?

1. Great Balls of _____
2. Roll Over _____
3. Taking Care of _____
4. Help Me, _____
5. I Got You _____
6. Duke of _____
7. The Lion Sleeps _____
8. Leader of the _____
9. Take Me Home _____
10. Leaving on a _____
11. Proud _____
12. I Heard It Through the _____
13. Bridge Over Troubled _____
14. The Wind Beneath My _____
15. _____ Bugle Boy

Scrambled Symphony

Unscramble each of the following words and phrases to reveal the name of a musical instrument.

1. groan
2. by clams
3. late grin
4. race lint
5. rent boom
6. on a boss
7. tug air
8. her long shin

9. Kurt melted
10. Brad's sum
11. an ox hopes
12. Roy baked
13. on a tribe
14. harm a coin
15. holy ox pen

Rainbow Tunes

What color word(s) will complete each of the following song lyrics?

1. a tisket, a tasket, a _____ and _____ basket

2. for _____ mountain majesties

3. _____ waves of grain

4. itsy-bitsy, teeny-weeny _____ polka-dot bikini

5. don't it make my _____ eyes _____?

6. all the leaves are _____ and the sky is _____

7. old _____ goose is dead

8. tie a _____ ribbon 'round the old oak tree

9. _____ rose of Texas

10. _____ suede shoes

11. she'll be drivin' six _____ horses

12. little _____ jug

13. _____ bells

14. _____, _____ grass of home

15. flying _____ people eater

Word Brain Teasers

Rearrange It

An anagram is a word that uses the same letters as another word, but in a different order. See if you can come up with an anagram for each of the words below. Some words have more than one anagram.

Example:

stop → pots, spot, tops, post, opts

1. march	11. heart	21. miles
2. slot	12. team	22. field
3. sword	13. bread	23. rated
4. there	14. pale	24. baker
5. slate	15. once	25. stake
6. drawer	16. petal	26. trace
7. tide	17. star	27. bleat
8. panel	18. side	28. coast
9. organ	19. softer	29. cares
10. wolf	20. space	30. dimple

Word Jumble

Make a list of words that . . .

1. are *palindromes* (words that read the same forward or backward; e.g., noon, madam, radar).
2. make a new word when letters are reversed (e.g., tar, pan, snip).
3. are *homophones* (words that sound the same but are spelled differently; e.g., sea-see, pain-pane, chants-chance).
4. are *homographs* (words that are spelled the same but sound different; e.g., I will *read* the book tomorrow. Last night I *read* the newspaper. The *record* was broken. I will *record* the music).
5. start and end with the same letter.
6. have three or more of the same letter.
7. have three different vowels.
8. contain the word *cat* or the word *dog* (e.g., Catholic, scat, dogma).
9. are compound words containing a color word (e.g., redhead, greenhouse, black eye).
10. have a short vowel that changes to a long vowel if you add an "e" to the end (e.g., spin-spine, Dan-Dane, Sam-same, cut-cute).

73

Alliteration

A sentence uses alliteration when each word in the sentence begins with the same letter. Think of an alliterative sentence of five or more words using each letter below. Use your imagination!

Example:

G — Gobbling goldfish give great gifts.

1. T
2. S
3. R
4. M
5. P

6. N
7. B
8. W
9. C
10. D

"De-tailed" Words

How many words can you come up with that leave a new word when their "tails" (last letter) are removed? (Removing the final "s" from a plural doesn't count.)

Example:

The word "hearth" becomes "heart" if the final "h" is removed.

Warm-ups:

Begin with a word of the given length and make a new word by dropping the last letter.

Start with a . . .
1. four-letter word
2. five-letter word
3. six-letter word
4. seven-letter word

Challenge:

What is the longest list of rhyming words you can come up with in which each word on the list makes a new word when its last letter is removed?

Example:

Rhyming words: heart-cart-start-mart-Bart-part-tart
Become: hear-car-star-mar-bar-par-tar

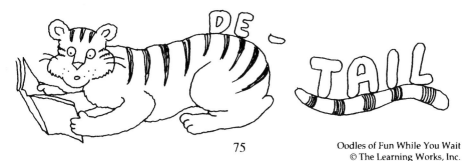

75

Br<u>ain</u>**storm**

How many ways can you hide each of these small words in a larger word? The word may be hidden at the beginning, in the middle, or at the end of the larger word.

Example:

and → <u>And</u>es, squ<u>and</u>er, br<u>and</u>

1.	rain	11.	am
2.	all	12.	an
3.	red	13.	man
4.	are	14.	ton
5.	ant	15.	as
6.	be	16.	one
7.	to	17.	ran
8.	on	18.	her
9.	can	19.	do
10.	ham	20.	me

Baby, Baby

What is each of the following animal babies called?

Example:

a baby **dog** is called a **puppy**

1. frog
2. duck
3. eagle
4. kangaroo
5. lion
6. rabbit
7. sheep
8. deer
9. pig
10. goat

11. horse
12. goose
13. cow
14. cat
15. elephant
16. chicken
17. fox
18. whale
19. bear
20. swan

First and Last

Make two compound words from each word below. Think of a word that you can add to the beginning for one compound and another word to add to the end for a second compound.

Example:

<u>SURE</u> **FIRE** <u>FLY</u>

1. _____LIGHT_____
2. _____DAY_____
3. _____PAPER_____
4. _____BATH_____
5. _____DOG_____
6. _____ROOM_____
7. _____SIDE_____
8. _____COAT_____
9. _____FOOT_____
10. _____NIGHT_____
11. _____OVER_____
12. _____MAN_____
13. _____CAKE_____
14. _____TOWN_____
15. _____FLOWER_____

Rare Pairs

Think of a pair of rhyming words that means the same as each of the following descriptions.

Example:

fake hair for a porker → pig wig

1. furry yellow bird
2. overweight feline
3. phony rattler
4. law-abiding national bird
5. slow-moving creature's bucket
6. off-road vehicle for a ewe
7. unique cub
8. picnic pest's trousers
9. baby cat's gloves
10. nanny's jacket
11. rodent's dwelling
12. young female bushy-tailed rodent
13. blackbird's stockings
14. curtains for a monkey
15. long-necked creature's giggle

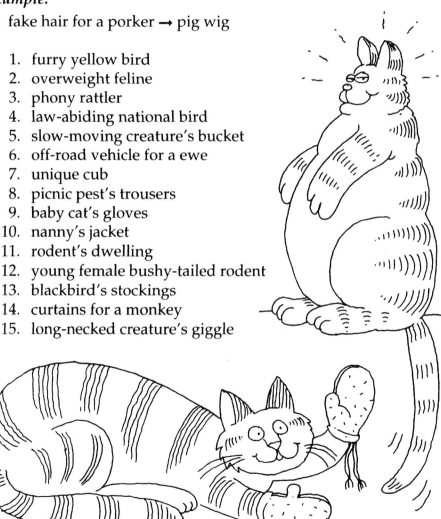

79

Finish That Thought

Can you come up with a funny ending for each of these sayings?

1. Don't bite off more than _____ .

2. He who laughs last _____ .

3. A bird in the hand _____ .

4. The more things change _____ .

5. It's not over 'til _____ .

6. The bigger they are _____ .

7. The early bird _____ .

8. A penny saved _____ .

9. People who live in glass houses _____ .

10. The grass is always greener _____ .

11. It's always darkest _____ .

12. A rolling stone _____ .

13. You can't judge a book _____ .

14. The older you get _____ .

15. Slow and steady _____ .

Animal Compound

An animal's name placed in each blank below will create a compound word that means the same as the clue to its left.

Example:

hard worker → eager beaver

1.	short snooze	_____nap
2.	mushroom	_____stool
3.	target	_____'s eye
4.	carpenter's helper	saw_____
5.	scuba diver	_____man
6.	braids	_____tails
7.	wrangler	_____boy
8.	beginner's swim stroke	_____paddle
9.	long, high hit	_____ball
10.	high-collared shirt	_____neck
11.	megaphone	_____horn
12.	not favored to win	under_____
13.	eat too much	_____-out
14.	bent pages	_____-eared
15.	string game	_____'s cradle

Alphabet Trivia

How long a list can you brainstorm for each of the following?

1. girls' names beginning with the letter "D"
2. countries beginning with the letter "S"
3. occupations beginning with the letter "T"
4. cities beginning with the letter "M"
5. mammals beginning with the letter "M"
6. fruits beginning with the letter "P"
7. sports beginning with the letter "B"
8. vegetables beginning with the letter "C"
9. "sweet stuff" beginning with the letter "P"
10. things to wear beginning with the letter "S"

Four-Letter Fun

How many four-letter words can you name
in each of the following categories?

1. boys' names
2. foods
3. animals
4. colors
5. weather words
6. things to wear
7. girls' names
8. sharp things
9. things that are hot
10. containers
11. body parts
12. things in the sky
13. white things
14. ends with the letter "d"
15. begins with the letter "c"
16. has "oo" in the middle
17. has "ea" in the middle
18. geography words
19. begins and ends with "t"
20. things that would fit in your hand

Oodles of Fun While You Wait
© The Learning Works, Inc.

Over and Over Again

How many new uses can you think of for...

1. a sock with a hole in it?
2. a plastic milk jug?
3. a paper plate?
4. a wire hanger?
5. a brick?
6. an old magazine?
7. a yardstick?
8. an egg carton?
9. a tennis ball?
10. Sunday's newspaper?
11. an old tire?
12. a pillowcase?
13. a soda can?
14. a glass jar?
15. a tissue box?
16. a toothbrush?
17. a clothespin?
18. a picture frame?
19. a salt shaker?
20. a dozen buttons?

Rhyme and Reason

How long a list of rhyming words can you come up with for each of the following words?

Example:

back → black, crack, hack, hijack, Jack, knack, lack, Mac, pack, quack, rack, sack, stack, tack, track, unpack, whack, yak, Zach

1. and	11. oh
2. it	12. eight
3. went	13. bed
4. bite	14. pan
5. end	15. cane
6. at	16. out
7. one	17. I
8. dog	18. side
9. nine	19. in
10. pay	20. ace

85

S-T-R-E-T-C-H Your Brain

How long a list of words can you brainstorm that fit each of the following categories? How many things can you think of that . . .

1. are white?
2. are red?
3. are green?
4. are black?
5. are yellow?
6. have words on them?
7. you can put things into?
8. open and close?
9. will fit in your hand?
10. have numbers on them?
11. have doors?
12. come on a roll?
13. have pages?
14. have buttons?
15. come in a box?
16. can be folded?
17. are cold?
18. are round?
19. are sharp?
20. have legs?

All in the Family

The first column shows three words that have something in common. The second column shows three words that do not fit in the group. Can you think of at least one new word that *will* fit in the first group?

MEMBERS	NON-MEMBERS
1. white, brown, black	red, yellow, pink
2. tuba, trumpet, saxophone	piano, guitar, drum
3. Judy, John, Sara	Tom, Robin, Phillip
4. marshmallow, sugar, salt	pepper, mustard, cocoa
5. F, X, E	P, R, C
6. E, C, B	M, L, R
7. March, November, October	July, August, June
8. mother, broken, saucer	mom, fixed, cup
9. whale, horse, bat	tuna, seahorse, canary
10. 134, 469, 258	301, 294, 132
11. piece, deal, scene	part, sense, sofa
12. toothbrush, purse, frying pan	toothpaste, wallet, mixing bowl
13. kayak, radar, madam	canoe, sonar, miss
14. 88, 97, 556	89, 96, 445
15. Donald, Bob, Lionel	Richard, Tom, Alex

Oodles of Fun While You Wait
© The Learning Works, Inc.

Easy as 1-2-3

How many words can you make
that add 1, 2, or 3 letters between the letters given?

1.	t __ e	t __ __ e	t __ __ __ e
2.	r __ d	r __ __ d	r __ __ __ d
3.	b __ y	b __ __ y	b __ __ __ y
4.	m __ t	m __ __ t	m __ __ __ t
5.	d __ m	d __ __ m	d __ __ __ m
6.	s __ t	s __ __ t	s __ __ __ t
7.	p __ n	p __ __ n	p __ __ __ n
8.	w __ t	w __ __ t	w __ __ __ t
9.	c __ t	c __ __ t	c __ __ __ t
10.	f __ n	f __ __ n	f __ __ __ n
11.	g __ t	g __ __ t	g __ __ __ t
12.	h __ r	h __ __ r	h __ __ __ r
13.	l __ g	l __ __ g	l __ __ __ g
14.	d __ d	d __ __ d	d __ __ __ d
15.	p __ p	p __ __ p	p __ __ __ p

Challenge:

Challenge your friends or family members to top your list!

Just for Fun

Read the examples, and then find a way to fit each of these place names into a creative sentence.

Examples:

The team bought a *New Jersey* for the coach.
I got *Georgia* new tie for his birthday.
I don't know the girl's name, but *Alaska*.
Iraq the balls before each game of pool.

1. Mississippi
2. Iowa
3. Little Rock
4. Idaho
5. Maine
6. Kansas
7. Fort Worth
8. Seattle
9. Arkansas
10. Utah
11. Hawaii
12. Tennessee
13. Juneau
14. Paris
15. Lansing
16. Lisbon
17. Delaware
18. Alberta
19. Poland
20. Iran

Lost and Found

Hiding in each of these words or phrases is the name of an animal. Unscramble the letters to see how many you can find.

Example:

trap hen → panther

1. shore
2. rose rot
3. balm
4. no slam
5. one plate
6. role pad
7. Dean's alarm
8. copouts
9. fig fear
10. the panel

11. cried cool
12. log rail
13. any car
14. hold pin
15. golf dish
16. pine gun
17. saw eel
18. ate name
19. cup or pine
20. log a trail

Storybook Characters and Such

He or She?

Sometimes characters have unusual names. Tell whether each of the following characters is male or female.

1. Beezus in *Ramona the Pest*
2. Fudge in *Tales of a Fourth Grade Nothing*
3. the title character in *Maniac Magee*
4. Karana in *Island of the Blue Dolphins*
5. Tootsie in *Superfudge*
6. Leigh in *Dear Mr. Henshaw*
7. The title character in *The Great Gilly Hopkins*
8. Sponge in *James and the Giant Peach*
9. Omri in *The Secret of the Indian*
10. Veruca Salt in *Charlie and the Chocolate Factory*
11. Caractacus Pott in *Chitty Chitty Bang Bang*
12. Bando in *My Side of the Mountain*
13. Milo in *The Phantom Tollbooth*
14. Pippi in *Pippi Longstocking*
15. Attean in *The Sign of the Beaver*

Colorful Titles

What color word is missing from each book title below?

1. *Harold and the _____ Crayon*
2. *Where the _____ Fern Grows*
3. *Island of the _____ Dolphins*
4. *_____ Eggs and Ham*
5. *The _____ Pony*
6. *Anne of _____ Gables*
7. *_____ Beauty*
8. *Encyclopedia _____ Saves the Day*
9. *_____ Snow, Bright Snow*
10. *The _____ King*
11. *A Fine _____ Dust*
12. *Those Happy _____ Years*
13. *The _____ Stallion*
14. *_____ Fang*
15. *The _____ Pearl*

Oodles of Fun While You Wait
© The Learning Works, Inc.

Small Stuff

Each of the following characters has the word "Little" in his or her name. Read the description and name the character.

1. She lost her sheep.
2. They tried to build their own homes.
3. She went to visit her sick grandmother.
4. She thought the sky was falling.
5. He sat in the corner.
6. He thought he could. He thought he could.
7. He blew his horn.
8. Rodent born to human parents.
9. They lost their mittens.
10. She ate curds and whey.
11. Her father's death forced her to live in an orphanage.
12. They were tiny people, no bigger than a thimble.
13. He sings for his supper.
14. He laughed when the cow jumped over the moon.
15. She was adopted by Daddy Warbucks.

Animal Characters

Each of the following animals is a character in a favorite children's book. Tell what kind of animal each character is.

1. Ribsy in *Henry and Ribsy*
2. Wilbur in *Charlotte's Web*
3. Ralph in *Runaway Ralph*
4. Misty in *Misty of Chincoteague*
5. Tucker in *The Cricket in Times Square*
6. Searchlight in *Stone Fox*
7. Brighty in *Brighty of the Grand Canyon*
8. Dribble in *Tales of a Fourth Grade Nothing*
9. The title character in *Rascal*
10. The title character in *Abel's Island*
11. The title character in *White Fang*
12. The title character in *Corduroy*
13. The title character in *Sounder*
14. Picky-Picky in *Ramona and Her Father*
15. The title character in *Curious George*

Oodles of Fun While You Wait
© The Learning Works, Inc.

Let's Eat!

Each of these book titles is missing the name
of something to eat. How many can you name?

1. *Charlie and the _____ Factory*

2. *_____ Girl*

3. *_____ for Sal*

4. *The Enormous _____*

5. *Stone _____*

6. *James and the Giant _____*

7. *Freckle _____*

8. *_____ John*

9. *The Adventures of _____ Finn*

10. *On the Banks of _____ Creek*

11. *Rechenka's _____*

12. *If You Give a Mouse a _____*

13. *Cloudy with a Chance of _____*

14. *_____ Fever*

15. *A Taste of _____*

16. *Green _____ and _____*

17. *The _____ and the Arrow*

18. *_____ -a-Mania*

19. *How to Eat Fried _____*

20. *The Stinky _____ Man*

Big Game Hunt

Each of the following book titles is missing the name of an animal. How many can you name?

1. *One-Eyed* _____
2. *Sign of the* _____
3. *Mr. Popper's* _____
4. *Stone* _____
5. *The Reluctant* _____
6. *The* _____ *in Times Square*
7. *Trumpet of the* _____
8. *How to Eat Fried* _____
9. *The Velveteen* _____
10. *Make Way for* _____
11. _____ *and* _____ *Together*
12. *The* _____ *and the Motorcycle*
13. *Island of the Blue* _____
14. *The* _____ *, the Witch, and the Wardrobe*
15. *Mrs. Frisby and the* _____ *of NIMH*
16. *Clifford the Big Red* _____
17. _____ *Boy*
18. *Shadow of a* _____
19. *Julie of the* _____
20. *Why* _____ *Buzz in People's Ears*

Headlines from Literature

Each of the following "news" headlines might have come from a children's book. Name the book.

1. Strange Web Writing Draws Crowd at Zuckerman Farm
2. Girls Convince Father to Stop Smoking
3. Frontier Children Welcome Mail-Order Stepmother
4. Indian Girl Stranded for 18 Years on Deserted Island
5. Mouse Born to Human Parents!
6. Young Pioneer Girl Travels Through Connecticut Wilderness
7. Boy Lives Alone in Hollow Tree
8. Boy Survives in Maine Wilderness with Help from Local Indians
9. Cyclone Transports Kansas Farm Girl to Magical Land
10. Boy Wins Dogsled Race, Saves Grandfather's Farm
11. Girl's Family Loses Home During Dust Bowl Catastrophe
12. Boy Adopts Orphaned Fawn
13. Catskills Man Takes Twenty-Year Nap
14. West Virginia Boy Befriends Stray Dog
15. Mouse Takes Up Residence in Irwin J. Sneed Elementary School

Nursery Rhyme Riddles

What nursery rhyme character
fits each of the following descriptions?

1. He huffed and he puffed.
2. A spider sat beside her.
3. He jumped over the moon.
4. He broke his crown.
5. He jumped over a candlestick.
6. She could eat no lean.
7. She ate curds and whey.
8. He sat on a wall.
9. He put in his thumb and pulled out a plum.
10. She had so many children she didn't know what to do.
11. He was a merry old soul.
12. She went to the cupboard, but it was bare.
13. She had a little lamb.
14. He built a crooked house.
15. She was quite contrary.

99

Missing Persons

What first name is missing from each of the book titles below?

1. _____ *and the Giant Peach*
2. _____ *and the Chocolate Factory*
3. _____ *of the Wolves*
4. *Muggie* _____
5. _____ *Price*
6. _____ *the Big Red Dog*
7. _____ *and the Old One*
8. _____ *, Bangs, and Moonshine*
9. _____ *and the Purple Crayon*
10. _____ *and the Terrible, Horrible, No Good, Very Bad Day*
11. _____ *and the Magic Pebble*
12. _____ *Sleeps Over*
13. *Curious* _____
14. _____ *of Sunnybrook Farm*
15. *Saint* _____ *and the Dragon*

Seuss on the Loose

How many of these Dr. Seuss characters can you identify?

1. He had five hundred hats.
2. He stole Christmas.
3. He made scrambled eggs super.
4. He was king of the pond on the Island of Sala-ma-sond.
5. Her small, plain tail only had one droopy-droop feather.
6. He learned that the alphabet went far beyond Z.
7. Some were Star-Bellies and some were Plain-Bellies.
8. The world built a by-pass around these two stubborn fellows.
9. Mrs. McCave had twenty-three sons with this name.
10. Some were red, some were blue, some were old, and some were new.
11. He made green eggs and ham.
12. He helped Sally and her brother clean up the mess the three of them had made while mother was out.
13. He imagined he'd build the world's greatest circus behind Sneelock's Store.
14. He was a big-hearted moose.
15. Some have one hump and some have two.

Oodles of Fun While You Wait
© The Learning Works, Inc.

"Grimm" Headlines

What fairy tale does each of these headlines describe?

1. Wolf Impersonates Young Girl's Grandmother
2. Witch Climbs to Castle Tower on Ladder Made from Girl's Golden Braids
3. Miller's Daughter Spins Straw into Gold
4. Young Girl Escapes Angry Trio After Ransacking Their Forest Home
5. Queen Attempts Murder with Poisoned Apple
6. Tiny Visitors Spend Night Making Shoes
7. Trio of Porkers Outfox Housewrecking Wolf
8. Boy Trades Cow for Magic Beans
9. Wicked Witch Threatens to Bake Kidnap Victims
10. Princess Wakened from Deep Slumber by Passing Prince
11. Enchanted Fish Grants Fisherman's Wishes
12. Donkey, Dog, Cat, and Rooster Make Beautiful Music
13. Ugly Bridgetender Refuses to Let Trio Cross Bridge
14. Prince Finds Bride Because Shoe Is Perfect Fit
15. Kiss Turns Amphibian into Royalty

More Headlines from Literature

Name the title of the children's book
described by each of the following "headlines."

1. Young Danish Girl Saves Friend from Nazis
2. Brother and Sister Run Away to Metropolitan Museum
3. Dinosaur Hatches from Egg
4. Girls Cracks Egg on Head—The Yolk's on Her!
5. Teacher Attempts to Defy Gravity by Pushing Computer Out Window
6. Boy Discovers Enormous Fruit
7. Mouse Stranded on River Island
8. Young Boy's Toy Indian Comes to Life for First Time
9. Orphan Serves as Scapegoat for Prince Brat
10. Shaggy Burro Tangles with Murderer
11. Unhappy Orphan Meets Wealthy Guardian's Mysterious Son
12. Old Squire Forced to Sell Favorite Thoroughbred
13. Centerburg Youth Deals with Skunk, Comic Books, and Doughnuts
14. House Painter has Twelve Extra Beaks to Feed
15. Fourth Grader Wins Turtle; Two-Year-Old Terror Eats It!

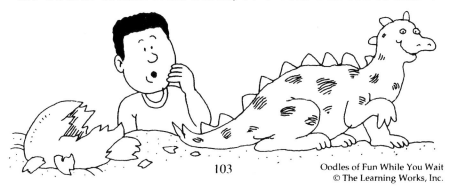

On Location

What story takes place at each of the following locations?

1. Birdsong Creek
2. Metropolitan Museum of Art
3. Villa Villekulla
4. Irwin J. Sneed Elementary School
5. Zuckerman's Farm
6. Misselthwaite Manor
7. Chincoteague Island
8. Stillwater
9. Centerburg
10. Mountain View Inn
11. Two Mills
12. Friendly, West Virginia
13. Freedom, New Hampshire
14. A-Z Antiques and Curio Shop
15. Potato farm in Wyoming

Point of View

Think about some of these familiar tales from a different point of view. Retell each story as it might have been told from the point of view of the character listed.

1. "Little Miss Muffet" from the spider's point of view
2. "Jack and Beanstalk" from the giant's viewpoint
3. "Old Mother Hubbard" from her dog's point of view
4. "Humpty Dumpty" as told by one of the king's men
5. "The Three Little Pigs" as told by the wolf
6. "Little Red Riding Hood" from the wolf's point of view
7. "Jack and Jill" as told by Jill
8. "Mary Had a Little Lamb" from the lamb's viewpoint
9. "The Three Little Bears" from Goldilock's point of view
10. "The Old Woman and the Shoe" from the shoe's point of view

Oodles of Fun While You Wait
© The Learning Works, Inc.

Answer Key

Page 8
License Plate Scavenger Hunt
Here are some possible answers.
1. talc, calculus, falcon, malice, garlic
2. barn, bear, Barbara, board, barrel
3. troll, Troy, strong, Castro, troop
4. solid, soldier, parasol, stool, scold
5. tree, tire, store, street, turret
6. crack, scrap, packrat, coral, Clara
7. cake, bakery, ankle, stake, streaked
8. string, straight, aster, oyster, ostrich
9. born, ornament, boring, corner, forlorn
10. pale, sprawl, appeal, corporal, playful

Page 11
U.S. Landmarks
1. South Dakota
2. New York
3. Massachusetts
4. California
5. Missouri
6. Pennsylvania
7. New York
8. Nevada
9. Illinois
10. Washington, D.C.
11. Virginia
12. California
13. Arizona
14. New York
15. Texas
16. California
17. Virginia
18. Florida
19. Washington, D.C.
20. Florida

Page 12
Naturally Wonderful
1. New York
2. Arizona
3. Utah
4. California
5. Alaska
6. Colorado
7. New Mexico
8. Wyoming
9. Florida
10. Kentucky
11. Florida
12. Georgia, Florida
13. Hawaii
14. Idaho
15. California
16. California
17. Massachusetts
18. New York
19. Oregon
20. Washington

Page 13
State It in Words
Answers will vary. Warm-ups:
1. was, wash, washing, a, as, ash, shin, hi, I, in, to, ton
2. new, ha, ham, a, am, amp, amps, I, ire
3. miss, I, is, sis, sip, pi

Page 21
Riddles for the Road
1. Rhode Island
2. Alaska
3. California
4. Michigan
5. Hawaii
6. Florida
7. Maine
8. Alaska, Hawaii
9. Connecticut, Delaware, Florida, Georgia, Maine, Maryland, Massachusetts, New Hampshire, New Jersey, New York,

Answer Key

(continued)

No. Carolina, Rhode Island, So. Carolina, Virginia
10. Alabama, Florida, Louisiana, Mississippi, Texas
11. Florida
12. Alaska, California, Hawaii, Oregon, Washington
13. Arizona, California, New Mexico, Texas
14. California
15. Alaska, Idaho, Maine, Michigan, Minnesota, Montana, New Hampshire, New York, No. Dakota, Washington, Vermont

Page 22
State of Being
1. Georgia, Kansas, New York, Texas, Utah, Vermont
2. No. Carolina, No. Dakota, So. Carolina, So. Dakota, West Virginia
3. New Hampshire, New Jersey, New Mexico, New York, No. Carolina, No. Dakota, Rhode Island, So. Carolina, So. Dakota, West Virginia
4. Alaska, Arkansas, Delaware, Florida, Hawaii, Idaho, Illinois, Iowa, Kentucky, Maryland, Michigan, Missouri, Montana, Nebraska, Nevada, New Hampshire, New Jersey, Ohio, Oregon, Rhode Island, Tennessee, Virginia, Washington, Wisconsin, Wyoming

5. Connecticut, Illinois, Massachusetts, Minnesota, Mississippi, Missouri, Pennsylvania, Tennessee
6. Hawaii, Tennessee
7. Alabama, Alaska, Arizona, Ohio
8. Alabama, Alaska, Arizona, Arkansas, Idaho, Illinois, Indiana, Iowa, Ohio, Oklahoma, Oregon, Utah
9. Alabama, Alaska, Arizona, California, Colorado, Delaware, Florida, Georgia, Hawaii, Idaho, Indiana, Iowa, Kentucky, Louisiana, Maine, Minnesota, Mississippi, Missouri, Montana, Nebraska, Nevada, New Hampshire, New Jersey, New Mexico, No. Carolina, No. Dakota, Ohio, Oklahoma, Pennsylvania, So. Carolina, So. Dakota, Tennessee, Virginia, West Virginia
10. Arkansas, Colorado, Delaware, Illinois, Kentucky, Maryland, Michigan, Missouri, Nebraska, Oklahoma, Virginia

Answer Key
(continued)

Page 23
What's in a Name?
Here are some possible answers.
1. Mustang, Cougar, Jaguar
2. Eagle, Falcon, Thunderbird
3. Ford, Omni, Jeep
4. Eagle, Buick, Dodge
5. Skylark, Thunderbird, Firebird
6. Civic, Altima, Cadillac
7. Corvette, Corolla, Accord
8. Eagle, Ciera, Fleetwood
9. Ford, Jeep, Dodge
10. Shadow, Taurus, Caprice
11. Century, Corolla, Horizona
12. Toyota, Mitsubishi, Nissan
13. LTD, Delta 88, Oldsmobile 98
14. Civic, Cutlass, Cougar
15. Eagle, Sundance, LeSabre

Page 26
Animal Actors

1. Pig		11. Bird	
2. Bunny		12. Piggy	
3. Woodpecker		13. Dog	
4. Mouse		14. Squirrel	
5. Duck		15. Pig	
6. Bear		16. Hedgehog	
7. Gorilla		17. Cheetah	
8. Panther		18. Mouse	
9. Rabbit		19. Moose	
10. Duck		20. Frog	

Page 27
Name That Kid
1. Opie
2. Adam, Hoss, Little Joe
3. Becky, Darlene, D. J.
4. D.J., Stephanie, Michelle
5. Rudy, Vanessa, Theo, Denise, Sondra
6. Judy, Laura, Eddie
7. Kimmy Gibbler
8. Steve Urkel
9. John Boy, Jason, Mary Ellen, Erin, Ben, Jim Bob, Elizabeth
10. Greg, Marcia, Peter, Jan, Bobby, Cindy
11. Richie, Joanie
12. Brad, Randy, Mark
13. Kevin
14. Samantha, Jonathan
15. Mike, Carol, Ben

Answer Key
(continued)

Page 28
Home Sweet Home
1. Bonanza
2. The Andy Griffith Show
3. Little House on the Prairie
4. Gunsmoke
5. Superman, Lois and Clark
6. Northern Exposure
7. Murder, She Wrote
8. Christy
9. The Flintstones
10. Saved by the Bell
11. Batman
12. Gilligan's Island
13. The Simpsons
14. Star Trek
15. Lost in Space
16. Step by Step
17. Happy Days
18. M*A*S*H
19. Major Dad
20. The Munsters

6. Darkwing Duck, Yogi Bear
7. Father Knows Best, Make Room for Daddy, Major Dad
8. Doogie Howser, M.D.; Coach; Magnum, P.I.; Dr. Quinn, Medicine Woman
9. Magnum, P.I.; WKRP in Cincinnati, L.A. Law, ER
10. Regis and Kathie Lee, Mork & Mindy, Barney & Friends
11. I'll Fly Away, Gilligan's Island, That's My Dog
12. Green Acres, Murphy Brown, Black Stallion
13. Designing Women, Reading Rainbow, Growing Pains
14. Funniest Home Videos, All Creatures Great and Small, Rockford Files
15. Golden Girls, Sesame Street, Reading Rainbow

Page 29
Mystery Titles
Here are some possible answers.
1. 48 Hours; 60 Minutes; Beverly Hills, 90210
2. Christy, Murphy Brown, Roseanne
3. The Dick Van Dyke Show, The Andy Griffith Show, Dennis the Menace
4. Matlock, Wings, Columbo
5. Chicago Hope, WKRP in Cincinnati

Page 30
Sidekicks

1.	Bert	11.	Mindy
2.	Clark	12.	Dr. Jekyll
3.	Tom	13.	Laurel
4.	Costello	14.	Clyde
5.	Mack	15.	Gretel
6.	Robin	16.	Jeff
7.	Pokey	17.	Bamm-Bamm
8.	Kathie Lee	18.	Ebert
9.	Roadrunner	19.	Dale
10.	Sears	20.	Lacey

Answer Key
(continued)

Page 31
Something in Common
1. each wears a mask
2. lawyers
3. each can fly
4. "Happy Days" characters
5. Donald Duck's nephews
6. all are green
7. all were stranded on Gilligan's Island
8. dogs
9. Ben Cartwright's sons
10. The Three Stooges
11. The Chipmunks
12. Charlie Brown's friends
13. members of the Addam's family
14. "Gunsmoke" characters
15. Teenage Mutant Ninja Turtles
    famous Italian painters

16. Evening Shade
17. Addams Family
18. Night Court
19. All in the Family
20. Addams Family

Page 32
Fun and Names
1. Happy Days
2. Leave It to Beaver
3. Full House
4. Happy Days
5. Cosby Show
6. Murphy Brown
7. Blossom
8. M*A*S*H
9. Saved by the Bell
10. Andy Griffith Show
11. Dr. Quinn, Medicine Woman
12. Doogie Howser, M.D.
13. Sesame Street
14. M*A*S*H
15. The Waltons

Page 33
Movie Madness
1. Ducks
2. Rabbit
3. Cat
4. Crocodile
5. Wolves
6. Dalmations
7. Mouse
8. Bat
9. Dog
10. Horses
11. Cuckoo
12. Lion
13. Lion
14. Panther
15. Mockingbird

Page 34
It's Just a Job
1. housekeeper
2. architect
3. doctor (obstetrician)
4. deputy sheriff
5. hardware store owner
6. football coach
7. policeman
8. store owner
9. housekeeper

Answer Key

(continued)

10. TV news reporter
11. morning TV show anchorperson
12. host of "Tool Time" TV show
13. stunt man
14. lawyer
15. actress

Page 35
Name That Number

1.	100	6.	76	11.	34
2.	21	7.	10	12.	3
3.	101	8.	7, 7	13.	2001
4.	8	9.	7	14.	3
5.	100	10.	80	15.	12

Page 36
It's Not Easy Being Green

1.	yellow	11.	white
2.	purple	12.	blue
3.	green	13.	blue
4.	blue	14.	pink
5.	green	15.	white
6.	yellow	16.	brown
7.	white	17.	black
8.	yellow	18.	green
9.	green	19.	orange
10.	yellow	20.	yellow

Page 37
Friend or Foe?

1. Popeye (foe)
2. Barney the Dinosaur (friend)
3. Yogi Bear (friend)
4. Batman (friend)
5. Bert (friend)
6. Kermit (friend)
7. Garfield (friend)
8. Bugs Bunny (foe)
9. Mickey Mouse (friend)
10. Porky Pig (friend)
11. Fred Flintstone (friend)
12. Bullwinkle the Moose (friend)
13. Winnie the Pooh (friend)
14. Jerry (foe)
15. Dennis the Menace (foe)
16. Tweety (foe)
17. Roadrunner (foe)
18. Charlie Brown/Woodstock (friend)
19. Winnie the Pooh (friend)
20. Bugs Bunny (friend)

Answer Key
(continued)

Page 38
Movie Trios
1. Aladdin
2. Pinocchio
3. Bambi
4. Dumbo
5. The Sword in the Stone
6. Alice in Wonderland
7. The Little Mermaid
8. Cinderella
9. The Lion King
10. 101 Dalmations
11. Beauty and the Beast
12. Sleeping Beauty
13. Peter Pan
14. Robin Hood
15. Snow White
16. Lady and the Tramp
17. The Jungle Book
18. The Aristocats

Page 39
Three's a Crowd
1. Gilligan's Island
2. Dennis the Menace
3. The Beverly Hillbillies
4. Little House on the Prairie
5. I Love Lucy
6. The Munsters
7. The Addams Family
8. The Honeymooners
9. The Andy Griffith Show
10. The Waltons
11. M*A*S*H
12. Facts of Life

13. Perry Mason
14. Happy Days
15. All in the Family

Page 40
Reel News
1. The Wizard of Oz
2. Beverly Hillbillies
3. Mrs. Doubtfire
4. Home Alone (Home Alone II)
5. Incredible Journey
6. White Fang
7. Chitty Chitty Bang Bang
8. Honey, I Shrunk the Kids
9. Iron Will
10. City Slickers
11. E.T.
12. The Shaggy Dog
13. Beethoven
14. The Lion, the Witch, and the Wardrobe
15. Jurassic Park

Page 42
And the Winner Is . . .
1. football
2. baseball
3. hockey
4. horse racing
5. soccer
6. bowling
7. auto racing
8. college football
9. bicycle racing
10. auto racing
11. golf, tennis
12. auto racing
13. yachting
14. golf
15. baseball
16. tennis
17. golf
18. boxing
19. tennis
20. horse racing

Answer Key
(continued)

Page 43
Name That Sport

1. basketball
2. basketball, hockey
3. baseball
4. football, basketball
5. wrestling
6. football
7. football
8. football
9. hockey
10. hockey, field hockey

11. hockey
12. swimming
13. volleyball
14. baseball
15. golf
16. boxing, baseball
17. wrestling
18. tennis
19. golf
20. bowling

18. track and field
19. track and field
20. track and field

Page 45
Birds of a Feather

1. St. Louis/Arizona
2. Pittsburgh
3. Atlanta
4. Atlanta
5. Baltimore
6. Philadelphia
7. Seattle
8. Phoenix
9. Toronto
10. Philadelphia
11. Chicago
12. New York/Winnipeg
13. Houston
14. Charlotte
15. Dallas
16. Detroit
17. Houston
18. Anaheim
19. Tampa Bay
20. Calgary

Page 44
U.S. Olympic Gold

1. figure skating
2. speed skating
3. track and field
4. speed skating
5. gymastics
6. swimming
7. diving
8. figure skating
9. track and field
10. gymnastics
11. figure skating
12. boxing
13. tennis
14. swimming
15. basketball
16. gymnastics
17. swimming

Oodles of Fun While You Wait
© The Learning Works, Inc.

Answer Key
(continued)

Page 46
Team Names
examples:
1. Jazz, Heat, Suns
2. Reds, Blue Jays, Blackhawks
3. Carolina Panthers, Miami Dolphins, Buffalo Bills
4. 76ers, 49ers
5. New York Giants, San Francisco 49ers, Los Angeles Rams
6. Trail Blazers, SuperSonics, Cowboys, Timberwolves
7. Lightning, Red Wings, Vikings
8. Red Wings, White Sox, Trail Blazers
9. Bullets, Bulls, Nuggets
10. Broncos, Giants, Cowboys
11. Oilers, Timberwolves, Knickerbockers
12. Jazz, Bills, Suns
13. Islanders, Cardinals, Timberwolves
14. Astros, Islanders, Oilers
15. Jazz, Heat, Magic

Page 47
Famous Figures from the World of Sports
1. baseball
2. swimming
3. track and field
4. football
5. baseball
6. track and field
7. golf
8. gymnastics
9. figure skating
10. golf
11. boxing
12. speed skating
13. tennis
14. baseball
15. auto racing
16. tennis
17. figure skating
18. baseball
19. track and field, golf
20. track and field

Page 48
Scrimmage Scramble

1. tight end
2. rushing
3. quarterback
4. offsides
5. touchdown
6. referee
7. receiver
8. huddle
9. scoreboard
10. safety
11. punter
12. extra point
13. pigskin
14. gridiron
15. fourth down
16. penalty
17. cleats
18. holding
19. decline
20. helmet

Answer Key
(continued)

Page 49
In Position
1. football
2. horse racing
3. football
4. basketball, football, hockey
5. baseball, softball
6. football
7. cricket
8. rowing
9. football
10. hockey (all types), soccer, rugby
11. football
12. football, basketball
13. cricket
14. ice hockey
15. soccer
16. baseball, softball
17. soccer
18. football
19. boxing, weight lifting, wrestling
20. football

11. men's gymnastics
12. archery
13. hockey, football, baseball
14. track and field
15. hockey
16. hockey (all types), lacrosse
17. track and field
18. golf
19. darts
20. wrestling, gymnastics

Page 50
Necessary Equipment
1. table tennis, canoeing, kayaking
2. football, golf
3. archery
4. croquet, cricket
5. pool, billiards
6. badminton
7. golf
8. men's gymnastics
9. bowling
10. track and field

Page 51
World Class Athletes
1. Great Britain
2. Italy
3. Germany
4. France
5. Austria
6. Germany
7. Germany
8. Ukraine
9. Great Britain
10. Germany
11. Romania
12. Canada
13. Brazil
14. Australia
15. Ukraine
16. Sweden
17. Soviet Union
18. Norway
19. Australia
20. Canada

Answer Key
(continued)

Page 52
More Sports Terms
1. football, soccer
2. basketball, soccer
3. baseball
4. ice hockey
5. football
6. basketball
7. ice hockey, football
8. basketball
9. bowling
10. tennis
11. golf
12. bowling, basketball
13. football
14. golf
15. football
16. football
17. hockey
18. baseball
19. football
20. football

Page 53
Sports Mix-Up
1. handball
2. badminton
3. football
4. golf
5. tennis
6. gymnastics
7. baseball
8. basketball
9. bowling
10. billiards
11. luge
12. bobsled
13. wrestling
14. lacrosse
15. archery
16. horse racing
17. karate
18. handball
19. soccer
20. speed skating

Page 55
Triple Play
1. Bobby Unser
2. Rick Barry
3. Jack Kemp
4. Joe DiMaggio
5. Bruce Jenner
6. Jim Courier
7. Dick Button
8. Frank Robinson
9. Sugar Ray Robinson
10. "Red" Grange
11. Tai Babilonia
12. Willie Shoemaker
13. Gale Sayers
14. Reggie Jackson
15. Joe Greene

Page 56
More Sports Legends
1. baseball
2. figure skating
3. football
4. basketball
5. basketball
6. golf
7. tennis
8. baseball
9. baseball
10. tennis
11. golf
12. auto racing
13. tennis
14. gymnastics
15. football
16. tennis
17. basketball
18. ice hockey
19. tennis
20. basketball
21. baseball
22. boxing
23. tennis
24. boxing
25. baseball
26. figure skating
27. auto racing
28. golf
29. figure skating
30. football

Answer Key

(continued)

Page 58
Famed Song Characters
1. Yankee Doodle
2. Billy Boy's wife
3. Clementine
4. Little Teapot
5. Aunt Rhody
6. Puff
7. this old man
8. the muffin man
9. the people on the bus
10. little puffer bellies
11. Old Dan Tucker
12. Sal
13. Dinah
14. Michael
15. John Henry
16. Peter Cottontail
17. Johnny
18. Brother John
19. Frosty
20. Santa Claus

Page 59
Who Goes There?

1. Johnny
2. Mary
3. Rudolph
4. Clementine
5. Danny, Billy
6. Susanna
7. Peter
8. Michael
9. Lou
10. Joe
11. Rhody
12. Mack
13. Bonnie
14. Dan
15. Jimmy

Page 60
Where?
1. in the dell
2. in the corner
3. in the old man's hat
4. down by the station
5. over the hill and far away
6. at the animal fair
7. to seek a wife
8. down by the bay
9. on my knee
10. gently down the stream
11. to town
12. down south
13. over the mountain
14. up the water spout
15. up above the world so high

Answer Key
(continued)

Page 61
Next, Please . . .
1. and Bingo was his name-o
2. singin' Polly Wolly Doodle all the day
3. you make me happy when skies are grey
4. all the live-long day
5. here is my handle, here is my spout
6. the birds and the beasts were there
7. where the watermelons grow
8. I lost my poor meatball when somebody sneezed
9. see the little puffer bellies all in a row
10. the monkey chased the weasel
11. ray, a drop of golden sun
12. old times there are not forgotten
13. where the deer and the antelope play
14. gently down the stream
15. I'd hammer in the morning

Page 62
Animals in Song
1. fly
2. old gray mare
3. froggy
4. doggy
5. kookaburra
6. the bear
7. Bingo
8. a billy goat

9. my little dog
10. six white horses
11. a horse, and a flea, and three blind mice
12. three blind mice
13. five little ducks
14. eensy weensy spider
15. little bunny foo foo
16. duck with a feather on his back
17. the horse
18. monkey
19. four and twenty blackbirds
20. big baboon

Page 63
Name That Tune
Here are some possible answers.
1. London Bridge, Jingle Bells, Three Blind Mice
2. How Much Is That Doggy in the Window? Are You Sleeping? Do Your Ears Hang Low?
3. Ten Little Indians, 76 Trombones, Three Blind Mice
4. White Christmas; Rudolph, the Red-Nosed Reindeer; The Green, Green Grass of Home
5. Twinkle, Twinkle, Little Star; Big Bad John; Mary Had a Little Lamb
6. The Old Gray Mare, Old MacDonald, New River Train

Answer Key
(continued)

7. Mary Had a Little Lamb; Billy Boy, Jimmy Crack Corn
8. Bingo, Kookaburra
9. For He's a Jolly Good Fellow, I've Been Workin' on the Railroad, I'm a Little Teapot
10. I Left My Heart in San Francisco, My Old Kentucky Home, London Bridge
11. Hokey Pokey, Polly Wolly Doodle, Eensy Weensy Spider
12. Up, Up, and Away; Down by the Bay
13. The Farmer in the Dell, How Much Is That Doggy in the Window?
14. Rudolph, the Red-Nosed Reindeer; The Old Gray Mare, Little Bunny Foo Foo
15. Supercalifragilisticexpialidocious, Bibbidy-Bobbidy-Boo, Polly Wolly Doodle

Page 65
What in the World?
1. moon
2. grandmother's house
3. sword and pistol
4. pocket
5. the other side of the mountain
6. pipe, bowl, and fiddlers three
7. snow
8. pease porridge
9. basket of posies, garland of lilies, gift of red roses, and a bunch of blue ribbon

10. gum tree
11. bags of wool
12. hot cross buns
13. bucket
14. silver buckles
15. feather bed

Page 66
Movie Tunes
1. Aladdin
2. Mary Poppins
3. Cinderella
4. The Little Mermaid
5. Mary Poppins
6. Snow White
7. Song of the South
8. Pinocchio
9. Cinderella
10. Mary Poppins
11. The Nutcracker
12. Wizard of Oz
13. Sound of Music
14. An American Tail
15. The Lion King

Answer Key
(continued)

Page 67
Missing Links
1. Dan
2. Brothers
3. Heartbreakers
4. Simon
5. Brooks
6. Boys
7. Dead
8. Houston
9. McEntire
10. Eric
11. Kenny
12. Pilots
13. John
14. Barry
15. Men
16. Jam
17. Presley
18. Zeppelin
19. Mac
20. Stones

Page 68
Golden Oldies
1. Fire
2. Beethoven
3. Business
4. Rhonda
5. Babe
6. Earl
7. Tonight
8. Pack
9. Country Roads
10. Jet Plane
11. Mary
12. Grapevine
13. Water
14. Wings
15. Boogie Woogie

Page 69
Scrambled Symphony
1. organ
2. cymbals
3. triangle
4. clarinet
5. trombone
6. bassoon
7. guitar
8. English horn
9. kettledrum
10. bass drum
11. saxophone
12. keyboard
13. baritone
14. harmonica
15. xylophone

Page 70
Rainbow Tunes
1. green, yellow
2. purple
3. amber
4. yellow
5. brown, blue
6. brown, grey
7. grey
8. yellow
9. yellow
10. blue
11. white
12. brown
13. silver
14. green, green
15. purple

Page 72
Rearrange It
1. charm
2. lots, lost
3. words
4. three, ether
5. tales, stale, steal, least
6. reward
7. diet, tied, edit
8. plane, Nepal
9. groan
10. fowl, flow
11. earth
12. mate, meat, tame
13. beard, bared
14. peal, leap
15. cone

Answer Key
(continued)

16. plate, pleat
17. rats, tars, arts
18. dies, ides
19. foster
20. paces, capes
21. slime, limes, smile
22. filed
23. trade
24. break, brake
25. takes, skate, steak
26. crate
27. table
28. coats, ascot
29. scare, races, acres
30. limped

Page 73
Word Jumble
Answers will vary.

Page 74
Alliteration
Answers will vary, but here are some examples.
1. Ten tiny tadpoles took turns telling tales.
2. Slimy snakes slithered slowly seaward.
3. Roxy rearranged Ralph's red roses.
4. My mother made me mix muffins.
5. Paula's pal Patrick picked plump peaches.

6. Nelly's nine nieces needed new needles.
7. Benny's Bakery bakes beautiful brown bagels.
8. When will Walter walk with Winnie?
9. Can Connie count cracked cups?
10. Dracula's dad doesn't dare drive.

Page 75
"De-tailed" Words
Here are some possible answers.
1. cart/car; rank/ran; salt/Sal; hiss/his; pale/pal
2. start/star; paste/past; slate/slat; clank/clan; scant/scan
3. flamed/flame; pastel/paste; Quaker/quake; slider/slide; smelly/smell; browse/brows
4. decided/decide; cursory/cursor; cleanse/cleans; thirsty/thirst; freezer/freeze

Answer Key
(continued)

Page 76

Brainstorm

Here are some possible answers.

1. rainfall, raining, brainy, drain-pipe, strainer, refrain, grain, train
2. allow, allergy, alligator, shallow, taller, calls, small, baseball
3. redecorate, reduce, redwood, shredded, Freddy, shared, admired, bored
4. area, arena, aren't, barely, shared, Karen, flare, spare
5. anthem, antlers, anteater, pants, chanted, mantel, slant, can't
6. bear, bee, beans, slobber, blubber, gibberish, cube, tribe
7. ton, tooth, toenail, stone, storm, cartoon, tomorrow, lean-to
8. one, onto, only, bone, don't, spoon, moron, melon
9. candy, candle, cannister, scant, uncanny, scan, toucan, pecan
10. hamper, hammer, hamlet, champion, chamois, sham, shame, shambles
11. amp, ample, came, stamp, named, dream, cram, camp
12. and, antelope, ants, sand, plant, mane, bean, groan
13. manly, manner, mane, command, demand, foreman, manipulate, manual
14. tone, tonsils, stone, buttons, crouton, piston, tonight, tonic
15. aster, astronomy, paste, smash, please, bias, alas, commas
16. one-way, money, telephone, abalone, shone, alone, done, pinecone
17. rant, ransom, trance, orange, crank, bran, rancid, transfer
18. here, hero, cherry, other, feather, heretic, somewhere, therein
19. dog, dough, door, candor, random, ado, dodo, doubt
20. messy, metal, hammer, chimes, simmer, home, flame, medal

Page 77

Baby, Baby

1. tadpole, polliwog
2. duckling
3. eaglet
4. joey
5. cub
6. bunny
7. lamb
8. fawn
9. piglet
10. kid
11. colt, filly, foal
12. gosling
13. calf
14. kitten
15. calf
16. chick
17. kit, cub
18. calf
19. cub
20. cygnet

Answer Key
(continued)

Page 78
First and Last

Here are some possible answers.
1. day LIGHT weight
2. Sun DAY light
3. news PAPER back
4. sun BATH tub
5. bull DOG house
6. bath ROOM mate
7. out SIDE walk
8. over COAT rack
9. big FOOT ball
10. over NIGHT light
11. turn OVER coat
12. fore MAN hole
13. pan CAKE walk
14. down TOWN house
15. sun FLOWER pot

Page 79
Rare Pairs

1. hairy canary
2. fat cat
3. fake snake
4. legal eagle
5. snail's pail
6. sheep's jeep
7. rare bear
8. ant's pants
9. kitten's mittens
10. goat's coat
11. mouse's house
12. girl squirrel
13. crow's hose
14. ape's drapes
15. giraffe's laugh

Page 81
Animal Compound

1. catnap
2. toadstool
3. bull's eye
4. sawhorse
5. frogman
6. pigtails
7. cowboy
8. dog paddle
9. fly ball
10. turtleneck
11. bullhorn
12. underdog
13. pig-out
14. dog-eared
15. cat's cradle

Page 82
Alphabet Trivia

Answers will vary. Here are some possible answers
1. Diane, Debbie, Dorothy, Donna, Denise
2. Sweden, Switzerland, Somalia, Spain, Scotland
3. teacher, trainer, taxidermist, taxi driver, tailor
4. Miami, Madrid, Mexico City, Minneapolis, Memphis
5. monkey, moose, mouse, mountain lion, mink
6. pear, peach, persimmon, pineapple, pomegranate
7. basketball, baseball, bicycling, badminton, bowling
8. cauliflower, celery, carrot, corn, cabbage
9. pie, pudding, pastry, popsicle, parfait
10. scarf, slip, shoes, shirt, skirt

Answer Key
(continued)

Page 83
Four-Letter Fun

Here are some possible answers.

1. Carl, Eric, Todd, Matt, John
2. corn, soup, cake, milk, meat
3. goat, fish, bird, moth, bear
4. blue, pink, gray, navy, gold
5. rain, wind, snow, hail, cold
6. shoe, sock, coat, slip, vest
7. Joan, Lori, Mary, Anne, Tina
8. fork, hook, nail, tack, barb
9. fire, July, heat, oven, star
10. vase, dish, bowl, case, hole
11. head, foot, hand, neck, nose
12. star, bird, Mars, kite, smog
13. snow, lace, eggs, milk, salt
14. wand, send, kind, bond, word
15. cast, coal, crow, clue, chip
16. cook, wool, soon, room, foot
17. bear, head, seal, mean, leak
18. gulf, hill, lake, east, city
19. toot, tent, trot, test, that
20. gnat, dime, lint, mint, fork

Page 86
S-T-R-E-T-C-H Your Brain

Answers will vary. Samples are given.

1. sugar, wedding dress, marshmallow, milk, pearls
2. stop sign, blood, cherry, a blushing face, rose
3. a seasick face, the Incredible Hulk, grass, frog, guacamole
4. Lincoln's hat, burnt toast, tar, licorice, punched eye
5. banana, sun, coward, mustard, lemonade
6. TV screen, junk mail, mailbox, newspaper, ticket
7. vase, bathtub, refrigerator, sink, envelope
8. door, mind, window, hand, mouth
9. dime, pencil, cotton ball, match, pebble
10. football jersey, license plate, page, remote control, calendar

Answer Key
(continued)

11. house, cupboard, car, closet, oven
12. stamps, sheet music, toilet paper, aluminum foil, sesame seeds
13. Senate, book, newspaper, magazine, pamphlet
14. shirt, remote control, microwave, telephone, cuff
15. tissues, cereal, board game, cough drops, detergent
16. letter, dollar bill, hands, clean clothes, towels
17. ice cube, mountain stream, Antarctica, rude people, winter nights
18. plate, planet, marble, circle, button
19. porcupine quill, stinger, ice pick, staple, arrowhead
20. chair, spider, bed, stool, horse

Page 87
All in the Family

Answers will vary. The common characteristic of the member groups and some possible answers are listed here.

1. [color words with five letters] green
2. [musical instruments you blow] clarinet
3. [four-letter first names] Rita
4. [white foods] coconut
5. [letters formed with straight lines only] H
6. [letters that rhyme] D

7. [months with the letter "r"] September
8. [two-syllable words] tractor
9. [mammals] dog
10. [three-digit numbers where each digit is larger than the previous digit] 567
11. [long e words] feel
12. [things with handles] suitcase
13. [palindromes—words spelled the same forward and backward] mom
14. [numbers whose digits add up to 16] 448
15. [men's names that start and end with the same letter] Greg

Page 90
Lost and Found

1. horse
2. rooster
3. lamb
4. salmon
5. antelope
6. leopard
7. salamander
8. octopus
9. giraffe
10. elephant
11. crocodile
12. gorilla
13. canary
14. dolphin
15. goldfish
16. penguin
17. weasel
18. manatee
19. porcupine
20. alligator

Oodles of Fun While You Wait
© The Learning Works, Inc.

Answer Key
(continued)

Page 92
He or She?

1. female
2. male
3. male
4. female
5. female
6. male
7. female
8. female
9. male
10. female
11. male
12. male
13. male
14. female
15. male

Page 93
Colorful Titles

1. Purple
2. Red
3. Blue
4. Green
5. Red
6. Green
7. Black
8. Brown
9. White
10. Grey
11. White
12. Golden
13. Black
14. White
15. Black

Page 94
Small Stuff

1. Little Bo Peep
2. Three Little Pigs
3. Little Red Riding Hood
4. Chicken Little
5. Little Jack Horner
6. Little Engine That Could
7. Little Boy Blue
8. Stuart Little
9. Three Little Kittens
10. Little Miss Muffet
11. Little Princess
12. The Littles
13. Little Tommy Tucker
14. Little Dog
15. Little Orphan Annie

Page 95
Animal Characters

1. dog
2. pig
3. mouse
4. horse
5. mouse
6. dog
7. burro
8. turtle
9. raccoon
10. mouse
11. wolf
12. bear
13. dog
14. cat
15. monkey

Page 96
Let's Eat

1. Chocolate
2. Strawberry
3. Blueberries
4. Egg
5. Soup
6. Peach
7. Juice
8. Onion
9. Huckleberry
10. Plum
11. Eggs
12. Cookie
13. Meatballs
14. Chocolate
15. Blackberries
16. Eggs, Ham
17. Apple
18. Fudge
19. Worms
20. Cheese

Answer Key
(continued)

Page 97
Big Game Hunt

1. Cat
2. Beaver
3. Penguins
4. Fox
5. Dragon
6. Cricket
7. Swans
8. Worms
9. Rabbit
10. Ducklings
11. Frog, Toad
12. Mouse
13. Dolphins
14. Lion
15. Rats
16. Dog
17. Crow
18. Bull
19. Wolves
20. Mosquitoes

Page 98
Headlines from Literature

1. Charlotte's Web
2. Ramona and Her Father
3. Sarah, Plain and Tall
4. Island of the Blue Dolphins
5. Stuart Little
6. The Courage of Sarah Noble
7. My Side of the Mountain
8. Sign of the Beaver
9. The Wizard of Oz
10. Stone Fox
11. Blue Willow
12. The Yearling
13. Rip Van Winkle
14. Shiloh
15. Ralph S. Mouse

Page 99
Nursery Rhyme Riddles

1. Big Bad Wolf
2. Little Miss Muffet
3. the cow
4. Jack
5. Jack
6. Jack Sprat's wife
7. Little Miss Muffet
8. Humpty Dumpty
9. Little Jack Horner
10. old woman who lived in a shoe
11. Old King Cole
12. Old Mother Hubbard
13. Mary
14. crooked man
15. Mary, Mary

Page 100
Missing Persons

1. James
2. Charlie
3. Julie
4. Maggie
5. Homer
6. Clifford
7. Annie
8. Sam
9. Harold
10. Alexander
11. Sylvester
12. Ira
13. George
14. Rebecca
15. George

Answer Key
(continued)

Page 101
Seuss on the Loose
1. Bartholomew Cubbins
2. Grinch
3. Peter T. Hooper
4. Yertle the Turtle
5. Gertrude McFuzz
6. Cornelius o'Donald o'Dell
7. Sneetches
8. Zax
9. Dave
10. fish
11. Sam-I-am
12. Cat in the Hat
13. Morris McGurk
14. Thidwick
15. Wump

Page 102
"Grimm" Headlines
1. Little Red Riding Hood
2. Rapunzel
3. Rumpelstiltskin
4. Goldilocks and the Three Bears
5. Snow White and the Seven Dwarfs
6. The Elves and the Shoemaker
7. Three Little Pigs
8. Jack and the Beanstalk
9. Hansel and Gretel
10. The Sleeping Beauty
11. The Fisherman and His Wife
12. The Bremen Town Musicians
13. Three Billy Goats Gruff
14. Cinderella
15. The Frog Prince

Page 103
More Headlines from Literature
1. Number the Stars
2. From the Mixed-Up Files of Mrs. Basil E. Frankweiler
3. The Enormous Egg
4. Ramona Quimby, Age 8
5. Wayside School is Falling Down
6. James and the Giant Peach
7. Abel's Island
8. The Indian in the Cupboard
9. The Whipping Boy
10. Brighty of the Grand Canyon
11. The Secret Garden
12. Black Beauty
13. Homer Price
14. Mr. Popper's Penguins
15. Tales of a Fourth Grade Nothing

Page 104
On Location
1. Old Yeller
2. From the Mixed-Up Files of Mrs. Basil E. Frankweiler
3. Pippi Longstocking series
4. Ralph S. Mouse
5. Charlotte's Web
6. The Secret Garden
7. Misty
8. Mr. Popper's Penguins
9. Homer Price
10. The Mouse and the Motorcycle
11. Maniac Magee
12. Shiloh
13. The Enormous Egg
14. The Egypt Game
15. Stone Fox